NATURE

This book belongs to:

I began this book on: (DATE)

I made my first I-Spy on: (DATE)

I sent off for my badge on: (DATE)

To get you started on the 1000 points you need for a badge, here are a few easy spots you can make now.

If you look 'Above your Head' what does Cumulus cloud resemble?
5 points for a right answer

In 'In Forests, Woods, and Hedges' what shape are the leaves of the Beech Tree?
5 points for a right answer

In 'Traces of the Past' what do Belemnites resemble?
5 points for a right answer

In the 'Mountains and Moorland' what shape is a valley that has been cut by a glacier?
5 points for a right answer

Answers on page 48

Cumulus

These are the best-known 'cotton-wool' clouds which, when they are small and on their own in the sky, suggest there is fair weather still to come.

I-Spy for 5

Cumulonimbus

As banks of Cumulus clouds build up, they should be called Cumulonimbus, and, as they darken, they will eventually lead to rain.

I-Spy for 10

Stratocumulus
These layered clouds often form as Cumulus clouds spread out across the sky. They may build up in thick, dark bands but usually lead only to showers.
I-Spy for **15**

Altocumulus
Altocumulus clouds form at high levels in the atmosphere and look like layers of small white to grey Cumulus clouds. These clouds indicate that the high atmosphere is damp and unstable.
I-Spy for **15**

Cirrus
The thin wispy streaks of Cirrus clouds are made up of ice particles and, as they thicken, this suggests the approach of warm air which may also lead to rain within 24 hours.
I-Spy for 15

Storm Clouds
As Cumulonimbus clouds build up to form an anvil shape with blackening bases, these are Storm Clouds and are a sure sign of heavy rain and even thunder and lightning to come.
I-Spy for 10

Mock Sun

Sometimes, bright coloured spots appear in a cloud on a level with the sun. These confirm that there are crystals of ice within the cloud which are bending the rays of light in the same way as a prism does.

I-Spy for 15

Rainbow

There is no 'pot of gold' at the end of the Rainbow. It is caused by droplets of water bending and splitting rays of light from the sun into the colours from which white light is made. What are the seven colours of a rainbow?

_____

_____

_____

_____

_____

_____

I-Spy for 15
Double with answer

Red Sunset

'Red Sky at Night, Shepherds' Delight'! This old saying is, to some extent, accurate: red may well suggest that there is good weather to come the next day. Farmers needed to know what the future weather had in store for them.
I-Spy for 10

Shooting Star

As a small piece of debris, called a meteoroid, falls through the Earth's atmosphere, it heats up and glows white so that it looks like a fiery streak shooting across the sky.
I-Spy for 50

Robin

You don't have far to
look to see a Robin.
Especially in winter,
Robins often turn up
in gardens. In
spring, they have
even been known to
nest in the pocket of
a jacket hung on a
garden fork.
I-Spy for 5

House Sparrow

These little brown
birds are perhaps
the most familiar of
all European
species. They have
learned to live with
people and to feed
on any scraps
that come
their way.
I-Spy for 5

Chaffinch

In some areas, such
as around picnic
sites, Chaffinches
may become very
tame and will come
right up to you and
even take food
from your
hand.
I-Spy for 5

Blue Tit

Blue Tits are famous for their acrobatics among the hedgerows as well as for their habit of pecking through the foil tops of milk bottles to drink the cream.

I-Spy for **5**

Great Tit

Not quite so acrobatic as the Blue Tit, the bold colours of this little bird make it instantly recognizable as does its 'Teacher-Teacher' call in spring.

I-Spy for **5**

8

Pipistrelle Bat

This tiny creature is quite common and, during the day, it may be found roosting in buildings and trees. It feeds on small flying insects which it hunts for over woodland, farmland, and moorland.
I-Spy for 30

Daubenton's Bat

About a quarter of the world's mammals are bats but they are not often seen. This bat is small and is found in woodlands. Bats will get caught in your hair. True or False?

I-Spy for 30
Double with answer

9

Deciduous Wood

With their tall, smooth grey trunks and pale green leaves forming a dense canopy high above, the trees of a Beechwood are a delight to walk among in spring. Deciduous trees lose their leaves in winter.

I-Spy for **15**

Coniferous Forest

Either side of a ride through a Coniferous Forest grow Larch and Scot's Pine Trees. Forests like this are often very dark and little grows among the leaf litter and pine needles on the forest floor.

I-Spy for **15**

Bark

Look carefully at the trunks of trees. You will see that the barks of trees are very different. A good idea is to use a wax crayon and sheet of paper to make bark rubbings. Look out for these three:

Ash

Sweet Chestnut

English Oak

*I-Spy **10** for each*

Ash

Sweet Chestnut

English Oak

Trees

Some trees have very characteristic shapes and live in particular places. Look out for the bluish green leaves of the **Atlantic Cedar** in ornamental parks and gardens and the beautiful **Weeping Willow** alongside lakes and streams.

*I-Spy for **20** for each*

Atlantic Cedar

Weeping Willow

12

Fallen Cones and Fruits

On the forest floor, look out for the cones and seeds of trees — they are all different. Here is a carpet of fallen **Scot's Pine** cones, the single cone of a **Norway Spruce** tree, and the open fruit of **Sweet Chestnut** — the ones we like to bake at Christmas!
I-Spy 10 for each

Scot's Pine

Norway Spruce

Sweet Chestnut

Scot's Pine

Norway Spruce

Sweet Chestnut

13

Compare the leaves

The appearance of the leaves of deciduous trees depends upon the season as well as on the kind of tree: in spring the 'sticky buds' of a **Sycamore** protect the delicate leaves; sunlight reflects from pale green, oval-shaped **Beech** leaves in spring; look for the heart-shaped leaves of **Lime** trees; the leaves of this **Field Maple** are turning golden in autumn. *I-Spy 10 for each*

Sycamore

Beech

Lime

Field
Maple

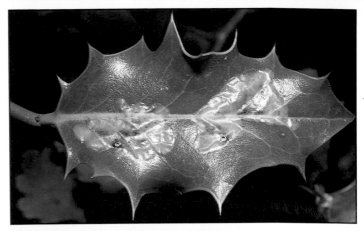

Holly Miners
It is the larvae of tiny flies which mine through Holly leaves and cause these familiar, irregular yellowish blotches.
I-Spy for 15

Robin's Pin-cushion
Not some strange kind of flower, this Robin's Pin-cushion Gall is caused by the invasion of a tiny gall wasp. It is found only on members of the Rose family.
I-Spy for 15

Red Pea Gall

Most gall wasps attack Oak trees. These are the so-called Red Pea Galls.
I-Spy for 20

Artichoke Galls

These strange growths look like Artichokes growing on an Oak tree but they are galls caused by the invasion of a tiny wasp-like insect.
I-Spy for 25

Bracket Fungus

This species of Bracket Fungus is growing on the stump of a Beech tree. Each type of Bracket Fungus usually grows on one kind of tree. They cause the wood to rot more quickly.

I-Spy for 10

Orange-peel Fungus

It is obvious how this brightly coloured fungus gets its name. This one is growing in a cleared woodland. Many kinds of fungus are good to eat but some are very poisonous. Do not eat any fungus unless you are sure it is safe.

I-Spy for 20

Common Puffball

This woodland fungus gets its name because, if it is tapped or broken when it is ripe, it blows out a cloud of dust-like spores.

I-Spy for 10

Stinkhorn

This strange-looking fungus gets its name from the foul smell it emits when it is mature. The smell attracts flies which feed on it and help to spread the spores.

I-Spy for 25

19

Wild Strawberry

The small red fruits of the Wild Strawberry are very sweet to eat. The plant grows in open woods on chalky soils and may start producing its white flowers in February in mild years.

I-Spy for 20

Cuckoo Pint

The small spikes of red berries which appear on this woodland plant during July and August are extremely poisonous and must never be eaten.

I-Spy for 10

Rose Hips

The orange or red fruits of shrubs of the rose family get their name from the Old English name for brier or rose. Hips are rich in Vitamin C and children are sometimes given a syrup made from the berries.

*I-Spy for **5***

Hawthorn

The berries of the Hawthorn tree are known as Haws. Haws are an important source of autumn and winter food for birds, such as finches and tits, as well as for some small mammals such as the Woodmouse. Country people sometimes call the tender shoots of Hawthorn 'Bread and Cheese'.

True or False?

*I-Spy for **5** Double with answer* ⸻

Elder

Elder trees may
survive in Rabbit
warrens because
Rabbits do not eat
the young plants,
and they also grow
near Badger setts
because these
animals eat the
berries but the
seeds pass
through
undigested.
*I-Spy for **10***

Blackberry

Everyone knows
that the ripe fruits of
the Bramble are
good to eat but not
everyone knows
that, even in Britain,
there are hundreds
of different kinds
which are all slightly
different from
one another.
*I-Spy for **5***

Crab Apple

It is from the wild Crab Apple tree that all the different kinds of eating and cooking apples have been bred. These little apples are rather sour-tasting but are often used for making Crab Apple jelly.

I-Spy for 15

Blackthorn

The dusty looking blue berries of the Blackthorn are often called Sloes and they are the ancestors of the garden plum. Sloes are extremely sour, however.

I-Spy for 15

Holly

People have used bright red Holly berries to decorate their homes in winter for generations. Only female Holly trees bear berries. True or False?

*I-Spy for **10***
Double with answer

Yew

Evergreen Yew trees are often found growing in churchyards. The seeds of Yew berries are very poisonous but many birds are able to eat the flesh of the berries.

*I-Spy for **15***

Ivy

Unusually, the purplish-coloured berries of the Ivy become ripe in spring rather than autumn. Like Holly, Ivy was thought to protect homes from devils and was often grown on houses.
I-Spy for 15

Roe Deer

Roe Deer are shy creatures, and they are all too easy to miss as they creep almost noiselessly through the undergrowth. But you might catch a glimpse of one as it crosses a road from one patch of woodland to another.
I-Spy for 30

Fox

Foxes are surprisingly common mammals and, although they are mainly creatures of wood and field, they now find their way into towns and gardens, and will even raid dustbins for food.
I-Spy for 20

Badger

Sadly, you are most likely to see a dead Badger, killed on the road. But, if you find a sett, you might be able to see one emerge from its entrance at dusk if you stay very still and upwind of the animal.
I-Spy for 50

Red Admiral

This large, brightly coloured butterfly is usually first seen in May or June but, although it is a Mediterranean insect, some individuals do manage to survive the harsh British winter.

I-Spy for 10

Comma

The Comma has tattered-looking wings for camouflage but it is the pale comma-shaped markings on the underwings which give this butterfly its name.

I-Spy for 15

Peacock

This large, brightly coloured insect may be seen during April and May and then again in September and October.

I-Spy for 10

Fossils are any remains or traces preserved in the rocks of animals or plants that were once alive, perhaps many millions of years ago.

Trilobite

A trilobite is an arthropod — an animal with jointed legs like an insect or a spider. Fossils of this animal are found in rocks more than 400 million years old.
I-Spy for 15

Graptolite

This fossil's name means 'stone writing' because, when it was first discovered, this is what scientists thought the fossils looked like. This one is at least 400 million years old.
I-Spy for 20

Sea Urchin

This is the 'skeleton', preserved as a chalky fossil, of a sea urchin or echinoid called *Nucleolites* (pronounced 'new-clee-oh-lie-teas') which lived on the sea bottom more than 120 million years ago.
I-Spy for 15

Lamp Shell

This Lamp Shell or Brachiopod is a member of a group of sea creatures that has existed for almost 600 million years. Why are they called Lamp Shells?

I-Spy for **15**
Double with answer

Ammonite

Anyone who has visited the beach at Lyme Regis in Dorset will be familiar with these fossils. The animals are extinct but they are related to modern squids and octopuses.
I-Spy for **10**

Belemnite

These fossils are also related to octopuses and squids but the bullet-shaped fossil is similar in many ways to the internal skeleton of a cuttlefish.
I-Spy for **10**

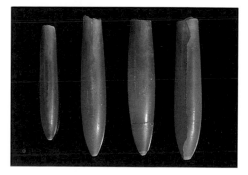

Rocky Shore

The bright-red cliffs and fallen rocks beneath are made from a rock called sandstone which, in this case, was formed some 250 million years ago when this part of Devon, England was a desert.

I-Spy for 10

White Cliffs

These white sea cliffs are made from a rock called chalk. It is not the same as blackboard chalk but was formed from the skeletons of many billions of tiny animals which lived in the warm seas of almost 100 million years ago.

I-Spy for 10

Sandy Beach

This kind of broad, gently sloping sandy beach occurs where the
swell from the open sea rolls in, deposits some sand and pulls
much of it back into the sea again. Steeper beaches usually
occur on smaller seas where the waves are smaller.
I-Spy for 10

Bouldery Beach

When rocks are
continuously
washed to and fro in
the water, their
original sharp edges
are gradually worn
away, and they
become rounded.
This takes millions
of years.
I-Spy for 15

Sand Dunes

These hills of sand build up behind sandy beaches where dry sand is blown until it is trapped by plants such as Marram Grass. Check the shape of the dune; it will show you which way the wind usually blows — shallow slope faces the wind, steep slope away from it.

I-Spy for 15

Shingle Bar

Where waves or currents approach the coast at an angle or are nearly parallel to it, sand and shingle are carried along the shore — this is called long-shore drift and may lead to the building of a spit or bar with a lagoon behind. What do we use to prevent the effects of long-shire drift?

I-Spy for 20 Double with answer

Sea Arch

A Sea Arch forms where the action of the waves hollows out a cave on either side of a headland. Eventually the two caves meet and the arch is made. The sea may then wear away the landward side of the arch, cutting it off from the coast.
I-Spy for 15

Wave-cut Platform

Wave-cut Platforms are formed at the coast as a sea cliff is worn back by the erosive action of the waves which undercut the cliff at first.
I-Spy for 15

Stack

A Stack is formed from an Arch because the continuous erosion by the sea eventually causes the arch to collapse leaving the seaward pillar of the arch isolated.

I-Spy for 20

Raised Beach

If you look carefully towards the top of what look like low cliffs behind some beaches, you will see that it is made of a shingly or sandy material. This is because that was once the beach and now the sea level has fallen in relation to the land.

I-Spy for 25

Folded Rocks

In this cliff at the coast, you can clearly see how the very layers of rocks from which the land is made have been folded into a wave-like pattern by forces heaving within the Earth's crust.

I-Spy for **20**

Schist

Look at this rock exposed in a sea cliff. It seems to glisten in the sun-light. It is a mineral called mica, which is formed by heat and pressure, that gives this layered rock its shine.

I-Spy for **20**

Fault

Rocks do not always fold when pulled or pushed by the Earth's forces. They may break, and such a break is called a fault. Here the fault, or line of the break, can be seen running from bottom left to top right.

I-Spy for 20

Bladder Wrack

There are lots of different kinds of seaweeds. Wrack is a general name given to certain kinds of brown seaweeds but do you know why it is called Bladder Wrack?

I-Spy for 10
Double with answer

Lichen

The yellowish patches and fuzzy green growths on the rocks are strange plants called Lichens (pronounced 'like-ens'). They grow on trees, rocks, or even buildings where the air is clean.
I-Spy for 15

Worm Cast

These are always worth looking for on a sandy or muddy shore. The coils of compacted mud or sand are made by worms living beneath which pass them out as they extract food from beach material.
I-Spy for 15

Star Fish

Among the animals that you can find at the shore, a star fish is one of the most exciting. Interestingly, if a starfish loses one of its arms, it can simply grow another one.
I-Spy for 20

Mountains

Mountains are higher than hills, usually more rugged and rocky, and notably higher than the land around. High mountains like the Himalayas were formed more recently than lower ones such as those of Scotland.

I-Spy for 10

Heathland

Heathland and Moorland are types of country where the most common plants are Heaths and Heathers. Some people think of Heathland as drier and at lower altitude than Moorland but both occur on acid soils.

I-Spy for 15

Firebreak

Because some areas, such as Heaths or Forests, may become very dry in summer, there is always a risk of fire. Workers cut clear areas through the Heathland to prevent any fire from spreading.
I-Spy for 15

U-shaped Valley

River valleys are normally V-shaped but, where the land was once in the grip of an Ice Age, the river valleys were carved out by glaciers into a smoother U-shape.
I-Spy for 15

Roche Moutonnée

Pronounced 'rosh moo-tonn-ay', this is a rock which has been smoothed and rounded by a glacier passing over it. The name comes from the word used for a French sheepskin wig which was fashionable in the nineteenth century.

I-Spy for **25**

Drumlin

A Drumlin is a whale-shaped mound of debris left behind by one melting glacier and then moulded into shape by the ice of the next glaciation. It gets its name from an old Gaelic word meaning 'mound'.

I-Spy for **25**

Cotton-grass

These cottony heads can be seen in boggy upland areas during May and June. The 'cotton balls' are made up of fine hairs which help to carry the seeds on the wind when they are ready to disperse.

I-Spy for **15**

Granite

Granite is an igneous (formed by fire) rock. Some-times great masses of Granite, called batholiths are forced into place and give rise to upland moors like Dartmoor. The weather carved exposed granite 'knobs' are called Tors.

I-Spy for **15**

Limestone Pavement

Limestone is a rock which can be dissolved by acid. Rainwater is slightly acid and where the rock is exposed, the rainwater opens up the natural joints in the rock by dissolving it away. The open joints are called grikes while the ribs of rock are called clints.

I-Spy for 15

Drystone Walling

In some areas, such as the Yorkshire Dales, limestone rocks are used to make walls without any mortar to hold them together. The bare hillside seems to have a 'net' of walls dividing it up into curiously shaped fields.

I-Spy for 15

Common Frog

The Frog has a smooth, wet, soft skin and varies in colour from greenish to yellowish. It will live anywhere which is damp but it lays its eggs in ponds.
I-Spy for 15

Common Toad

Like Frogs, Toads also breed in ponds. It is bigger than a Frog with shorter hind legs and a warty skin which is drier than that of its cousin. To what group of animals do Frogs and Toads belong?

I-Spy for 15
Double with answer

Mallard

The Mallard is a very common duck. It is found on rivers, streams, ponds, and lakes. This is the male bird, or drake, and he is much more colourful than the female.
I-Spy for 5

Mountain Stream

When rivers are close to their source in steeply graded land, they tumble through deep, V-shaped valleys in the mountains. These parts of a river are often called 'rapids' or 'white water'.

I-Spy for 10

Waterfall

A Waterfall forms where there is softer rock downstream from harder rock. The flowing river wears away the softer rock more quickly and the fall gradually gets higher. Which is the world's highest waterfall: (a) Niagara Falls; (b) Victoria Falls; (c) Angel Falls?

I-Spy for 15
Double with answer

Meander

In a flat valley floor where the gradient is shallow, a river will flow by swinging from side to side in a series of curves called Meanders.

I-Spy for 15

Lichen

You don't even need to leave the town to find interesting things growing. This Lichen (pronounced 'like-en') is growing on an old wall in a city centre.
*I-Spy for **10***

Spider's Web

After a frosty night in winter, go out into the garden and look for spiders' webs. You might easily find one with hoar frost on it looking like a gleaming necklace.
*I-Spy for **20***

Grass Snake

Grass Snakes may grow to 1 m (3 ft) in length. They live in grassy areas near rivers, ditches, and streams, and they are excellent swimmers. They do not have a venomous bite.
*I-Spy for **25***

Hedgehog

Hedgehogs are active mainly at night and you can sometimes hear them snuffling around a garden. They are good swimmers and surprisingly agile climbers.

I-Spy for **15**

Rabbit

You'll find Rabbits in most kinds of countryside where there is plant food for them to eat and suitable places for them to make their burrows.

I-Spy for **5**

Hare

At first glance, a Hare looks a little like a Rabbit but it is bigger with longer ears and legs. In spring, pairs or even groups of them can be seen dashing around the fields or even 'boxing' with one another.
I-Spy for 15

Mole

A Mole spends almost all of its life underground. You will be very lucky to see a live one above ground, but you can easily find evidence of them from the mole hills which they leave behind. What do Moles usually eat?

I-Spy a Mole Hill for 10
Double with answer

Fern

If you look on the undersides of Fern fronds, you can usually see little bumps. These are piles of spores which the fern uses to spread itself. The spores are often carried on the wind.
I-Spy for 15

INDEX

Answers

Title page: Cotton Grass.
Stony bullets: U-shaped.
Rainbow: Violet, Indigo, Blue, Green, Yellow, Orange, Red.
Hawthorn: True.
Holly: True.
Lamp Shell: Because some kinds look like ancient oil lamps.
Shingle Bar:
Bladder Wrack: Because of the air bladders which make its fronds float.
Common Toad:
Amphibians.
Waterfall: (c) Angel Falls in Venezuela 979 m (3212 ft)
Mole: Worms

© I-Spy Limited 2000

ISBN: 1 85671 219 2
Michelin Tyre Public Limited Company
Edward Hyde Building, 38 Clarendon Road, Watford, Herts WD1 1SX

MICHELIN and the Michelin Man are Registered Trademarks of Michelin

A CIP record for this title is available from the British Library.

Edited by Neil Curtis. Designed by Richard Garratt.

The Publisher gratefully acknowledges the contribution of Bruce Coleman Limited, Premaphotos Wildlife, RIDA Photo Library, Darviainen, Storm Dunlop, W C Dunlop who provided the photographs in this book. Cover and title page photographs: Premaphotos Wildlife.

Colour reproduction by Anglia Colour Ltd.

Printed in Spain by Graficromo SA.